Although we all have little cares,
They will never undermine us,
If we pause for inspiration
From great minds such as Linus!

With Many Friendly

Linus
on
Life

by Charles M. Schulz

Contents

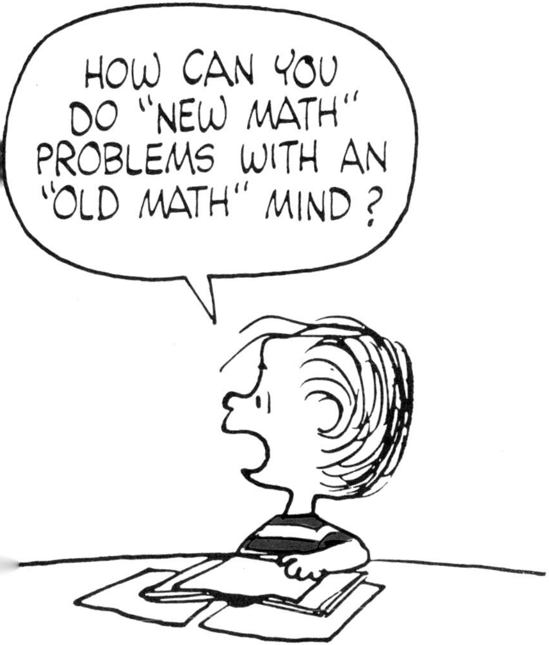
HOW CAN YOU DO "NEW MATH" PROBLEMS WITH AN "OLD MATH" MIND?

on Lending

on Being Prudent

Other Peanuts Philosophers
by Charles M. Schulz:

Snoopy's Philosophy

The World According to Lucy

The Wisdom of Charlie Brown

Layout by William Hunt and David Jenkins